D0514500

Essex County Council
3013030154137 0

'The Fortress of Fear'
An original concept by Elizabeth Dale

Illustrated by Erin Hunting

Published by MAVERICK ARTS PUBLISHING LTD

Studio 11, City Business Centre, 6 Brighton Road,

Horsham, West Sussex, RH13 5BB

+44 (0)1403 256941

A CIP catalogue record for this book is available at the British Library.

ISBN 978-1-84886-718-5

www.maverickbooks.co.uk

Gold

This book is rated as: Gold Band (Guided Reading)

The Fortress of Fear

By Elizabeth Dale

Illustrated by
Erin Hunting

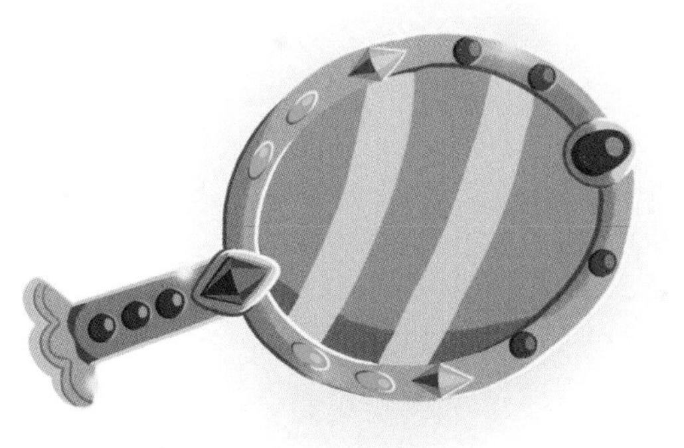

Chapter 1

“Tom, look!” Leo gasped. He shoved Tom.

“Hey!” said Tom, spilling his lemonade.

“Just look!” whispered Leo, pointing out of the coach window. And then Tom gasped too, as a dark grey building with spooky turrets appeared through the mist.

“That looks so scary!” he said.

“Right, kids!” called Mr Binks, as the coach parked outside. “I want you all to be on your best behaviour. There is a lot of history here at the Fortress of Forfar. Some say it is even haunted by the ghost of the fifth earl, searching for the priceless family heirloom that he lost.” Shrieks echoed around the coach. “Don't worry, there are no ghosts in the daytime,” their teacher laughed.

"I knew it was haunted!" said Tom, following Leo off the coach. A shiver went down his spine as he looked up at the grim walls and dark windows. A jackdaw fluttered out of the mist, making Tom jump. "That's not the Fortress of Forfar," he said. "That's the Fortress of Fear!"

"Come on!" laughed Leo, as everybody trooped inside. "Let's go in and get warm."

Chapter 2

But it was no warmer inside the fortress. Tom shivered as they walked down a long stone corridor. The suits of armour all along the walls seemed to be watching them. Then Tom realised something else was wrong. He tapped Leo's arm.

"I need to go to the loo!" he hissed urgently.

"Tom! We've only just got here!" Leo cried.

“I know! But I drank too much lemonade on the bus,” he said, wriggling. “There’s one near the entrance. Come with me, please, Leo!” He turned to their friend, Ella. “Can you tell Mr Binks that we’ve just nipped to the toilets? We’ll catch up with you.”

“Okay,” she said.

It was a lot further back to the entrance than Tom remembered. But they finally got there – just in time!

Afterwards, Tom hurried back ahead of Leo. He didn't want to get into trouble. But then he reached a staircase with corridors going in different directions. And there was no sign of the others.

“Where have they gone?” Tom cried.
“Mr Binks will be so annoyed!”

“Don’t know!” called Leo from behind him.
“Hey, look at me!” He jumped up and grabbed a long, gold rope beside a tapestry. But Tom strode away, anxiously looking for the others.

“Come on!” cried Tom. And then he looked back and froze. Leo had gone! Where was he? Tom hurried back down the corridor, looking for Leo everywhere. But there was no sign of him. “Leo!” he called, peering inside a suit of armour. But Leo wasn't there. “Leo! Stop messing around! Where are you?”

But there was no answer. A trickle of fear went down Tom’s spine. Leo couldn’t just disappear! He peered behind a chest and then inside it, but no Leo. He looked ahead, the corridor was long, but there were no doors along it. Tom rushed over to a large tapestry hanging on the wall and peered behind it. No one! He was really panicking now. Something awful must have happened to Leo. He'd been right. This really was the Fortress of Fear! And then he had a terrible thought...

Maybe the **ghost** had got Leo?!

Chapter 3

Tom looked around desperately. He had to get help. There was a long gold rope by the tapestry. Was that connected to an alarm? He pulled on it and suddenly, the stone wall started moving inwards. It was a secret doorway! Leo must be through there. He ran inside just as the wall closed behind him. And then, someone grabbed his arm.

"Aaargh!" Tom cried.

"Aaargh!" cried another voice.

"Leo?" Tom asked. He fumbled in his bag for his torch and switched it on. Finally, he could see his friend.

"Yes!" Leo laughed. "Isn't it amazing, Tom? I jumped up on the rope, the wall opened up and I fell in here!"

"You could have come back out and told me!" said Tom.

"It shut too fast and I couldn't find how to open it again in the dark," Leo explained. "I tried calling, but you didn't hear.

These walls are so thick!" He looked around him. "Hey, isn't this cool? A secret passage! I wonder if there's any treasure?"

"Never mind that!" said Tom, searching the wall with his torch. "We've got to get back to everyone, Mr Binks will be furious. We're going to be in such trouble."

“But we don’t know which way they’ve gone,” said Leo. “We’re in here now. Look, the passage goes that way, let’s explore a bit. Oh, this is so exciting!”

Tom would have argued with him, but he couldn’t see how to open up the wall again.

They were stuck!

Chapter 4

"Bring your torch, Tom!" called Leo. "I can't see where I'm going!"

Tom sighed and rushed after Leo along the narrow passageway, trying not to think of any spiders, rats or ghosts that might be waiting there...

And then, as Leo turned round the bend, Tom heard a shriek followed by a clattering sound. Was something attacking Leo?

Tom raced after his friend. Then he stopped in horror. Leo was sprawled on the floor – and a man in armour was on top of him!

“I bashed into this stupid suit of armour in the dark!” Leo muttered, getting up.

‘Is that all it is?’ thought Tom, as he helped pick the armour up. Then Leo gasped as the torch beam picked out something glinting on the floor.

“Look!” he cried, picking up a gold mirror encrusted with jewels. “This fell out of the suit of armour.”

“Wow, that’s so cool!” said Tom. He touched the gleaming handle of the mirror. But then he remembered Mr Binks. “We’ve got to get out of here fast!” he said. “But how?”

“Let’s just–aargh!” Leo tripped and fell against the wall. Suddenly, it started to open. He’d pressed a button by accident!

“We can get out!” Tom cried. “Come on!” He grabbed Leo’s arm and pulled him out. No sooner had they got through the wall than it closed again. Tom blinked and looked around.

They were back in a brightly-lit corridor. He could even hear talking. Up ahead, walking away from them, were their classmates. Tom smiled at Leo. What a relief! Except Mr Binks was going to be so angry...

Chapter 5

Ella turned as they ran up.

“Oh! Sorry!” she said. “I forgot to tell Mr Binks you went to the loo.”

Tom laughed. They hadn’t even been missed!

“That’s fine!” he said. Leo was about to show Ella the mirror, but Tom grabbed it and shoved it under his jumper.

"What are you doing?" Leo asked.

"No one knows we went for a wander, let's keep it that way," Tom whispered.

They continued around the fortress with their class.

As Mr Binks talked about all the interesting things they could see, Leo smiled at Tom. Mr Binks had no idea about all the interesting things they'd seen!

Finally, they reached the best part of any school trip, the gift shop!

“Come on!” Tom whispered to Leo, leading him out to the entrance desk.

The lady on the till was busy on the phone, so Tom quickly put the mirror on her desk while she wasn't looking. Then they ran back to join the others, just as Mr Binks finally did a headcount.

“Right, everyone back on the coach!” he said. “Well done for behaving. I hope you’ve all enjoyed yourselves?”

Suddenly, the lady at the till shrieked.

"The missing heirloom! It's here, on my desk!"

Everyone rushed to see. They all gasped at the mirror she held up.

"Maybe the ghost finally found it!" Tom said, winking at Leo.

Leo laughed. "Maybe!" he said.

The End

Book Bands for Guided Reading

Pink
Red
Yellow
Blue
Green
Orange
Turquoise
Purple
Gold
White

The Institute of Education book banding system is a scale of colours that reflects the various levels of reading difficulty. The bands are assigned by taking into account the content, the language style, the layout and phonics. Word, phrase and sentence level work is also taken into consideration.

Maverick Early Readers are a bright, attractive range of books covering the pink to white bands. All of these books have been book banded for guided reading to the industry standard and edited by a leading educational consultant.

To view the whole Maverick Readers scheme, visit our website at
www.maverickearlyreaders.com

Or scan the QR code above to view our scheme instantly!